# JOHN THOMPSON'S
# EASIEST PIANO COURSE
## FIRST CHRISTMAS TUNES

# Contents

# Teachers and Parents

This collection of popular folk songs is intended as supplementary material for those working through John Thompson's Easiest Piano Course Parts 2 and 3, taking the player up to Part 4.
The pieces may also be used for sight reading practice by more advanced students.

The material is graded, and has been specifically written to tie in with the program of learning as laid out in the Course books. Dynamics, phrasing and tempo indications have been deliberately omitted from the earlier pieces, since they are not introduced until Part 3 of the Easiest Piano Course, and initially the student's attention should be focused on playing notes and rhythms accurately. Outline fingering has been included, and in general the hand is assumed to remain in a five-finger position until a new fingering indicates a position shift. The fingering should suit most hands, although logical alternatives are always possible.

*John Thompson*

Arrangements by Lynda Frith

Cover design by xheight design limited
Music setting by Stave Origination
Printed and bound in the United Kingdom by
Caligraving Limited, Thetford, Norfolk.

Exclusive Distributors:
Music Sales Limited,
14/15 Berners Street, London W1T 3LJ, England.

Order No. WMR000210

# I Saw Three Ships

English traditional

# We Three Kings

John Henry Hopkins

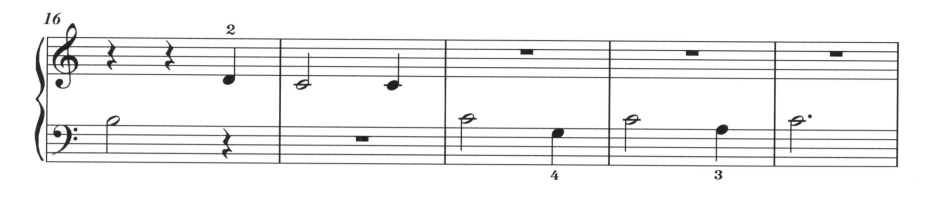

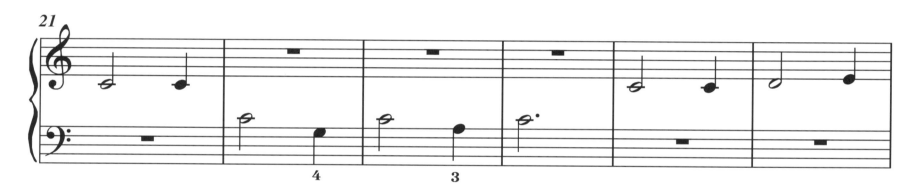

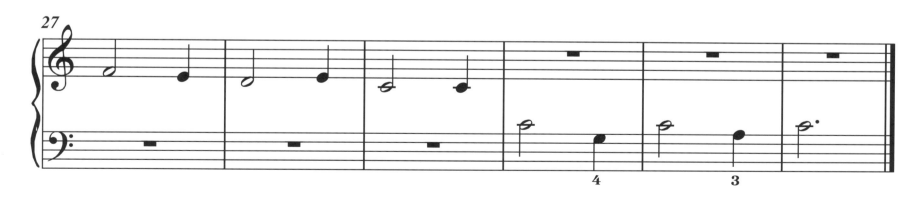

# Good King Wenceslas

English traditional

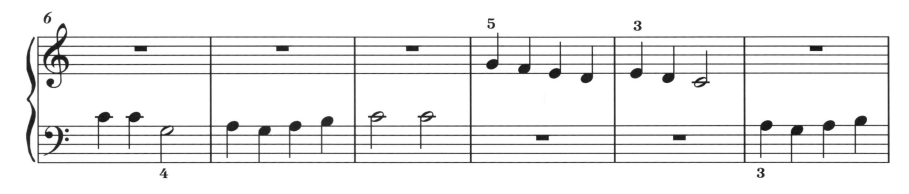

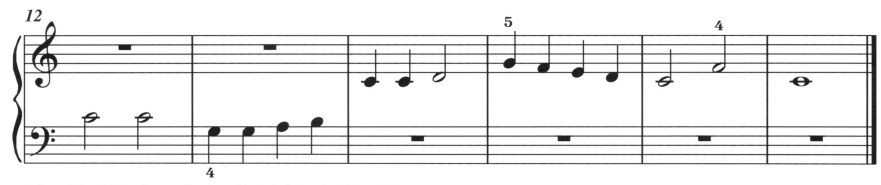

# O Come, All Ye Faithful

English traditional

# We Wish You A Merry Christmas

English traditional

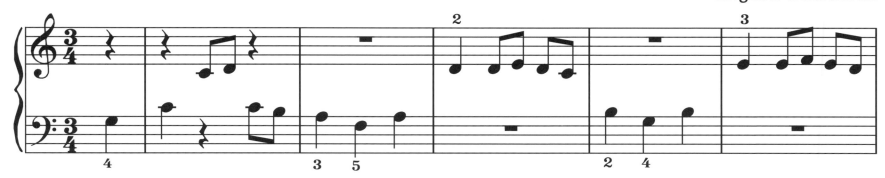

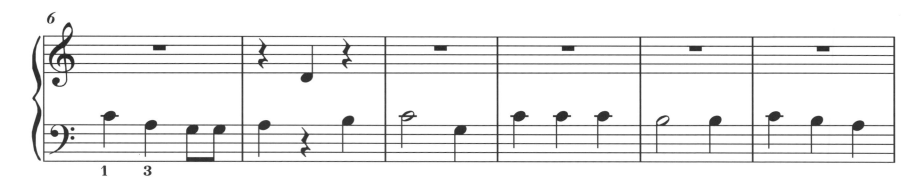

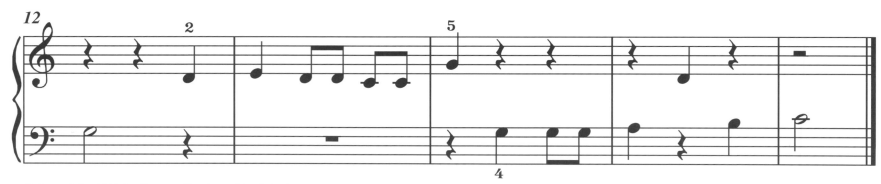

# Quelle Est Cette Odeur Agréable?

French traditional

# Lullaby Jesus

Polish traditional

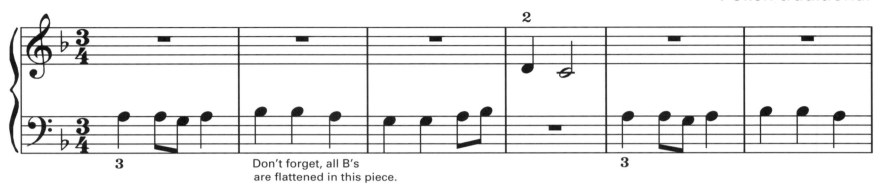

Don't forget, all B's
are flattened in this piece.

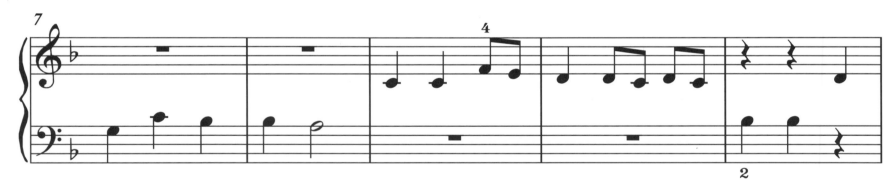

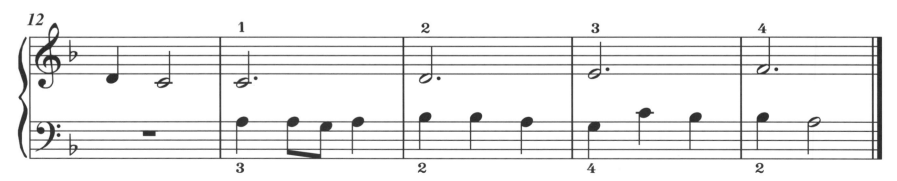

# While Shepherds Watched Their Flocks By Night

English traditional

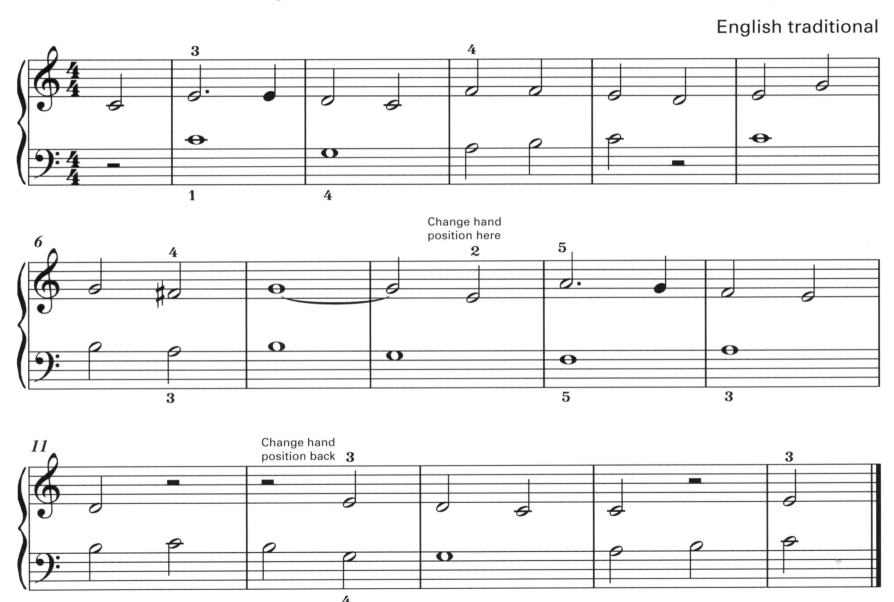

# Jingle Bells

James Pierpoint

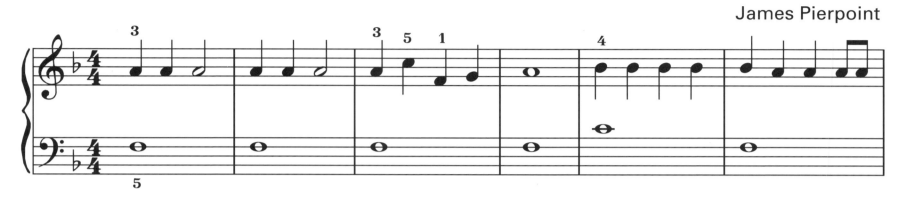

# Pat-a-pan

French traditional

# Il Est Né, Le Divin Enfant

French traditional

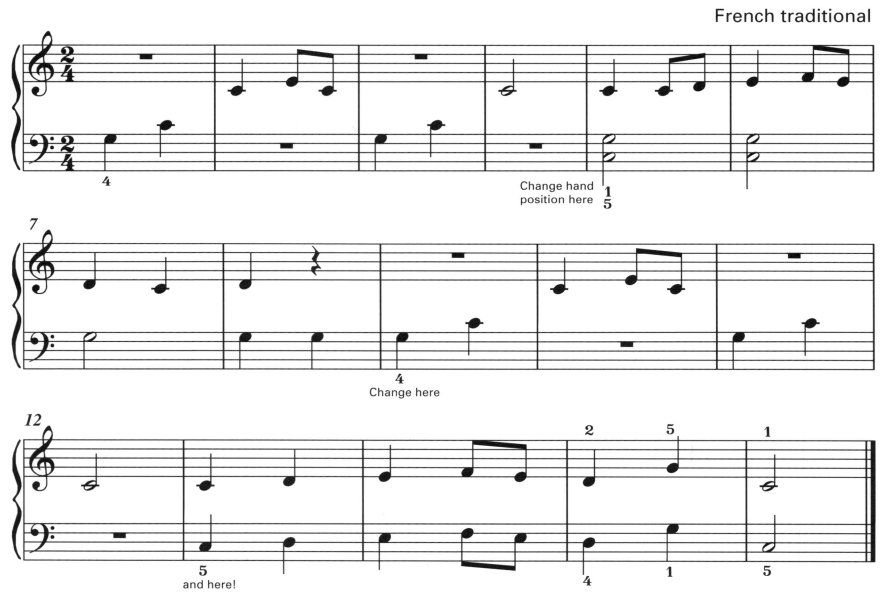

Change hand position here

Change here

and here!

# Andrew Mine

Moravian carol

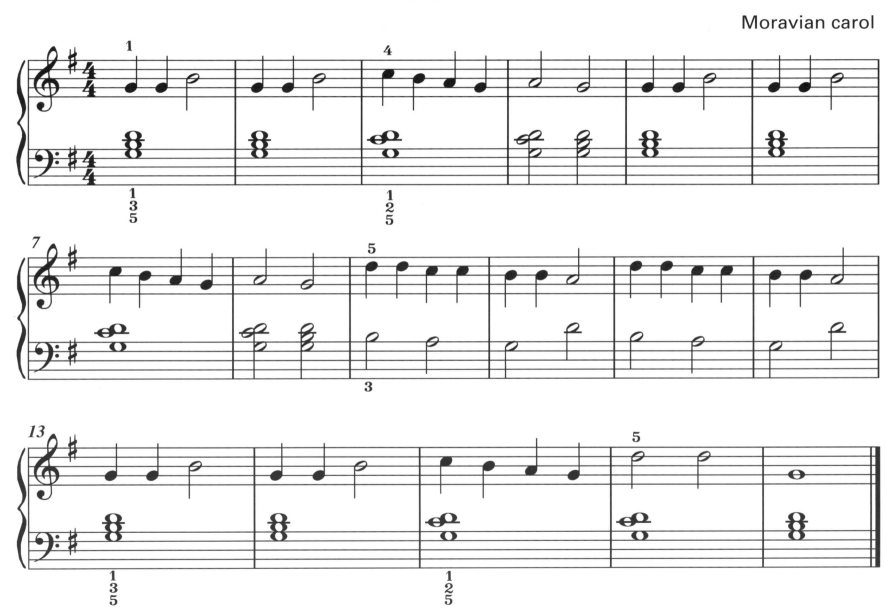

# Go, Tell It On The Mountain

American traditional

# Melchior and Balthazar

French traditional

# Sing, Shepherds!

Hungarian traditional

# Away In A Manger

W.J. Kirkpatrick

# Carol Of The Drum

Czechoslovakian traditional

# Deck The Hall

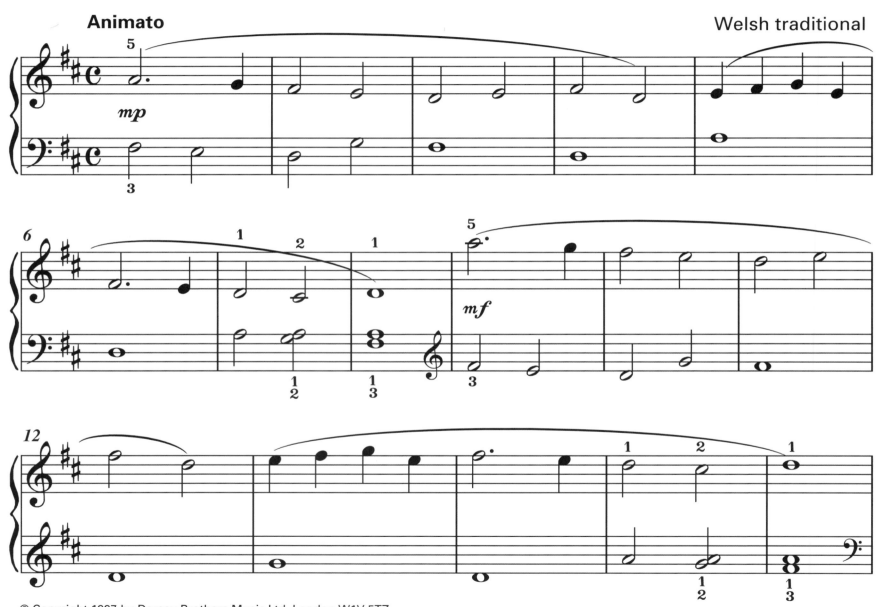

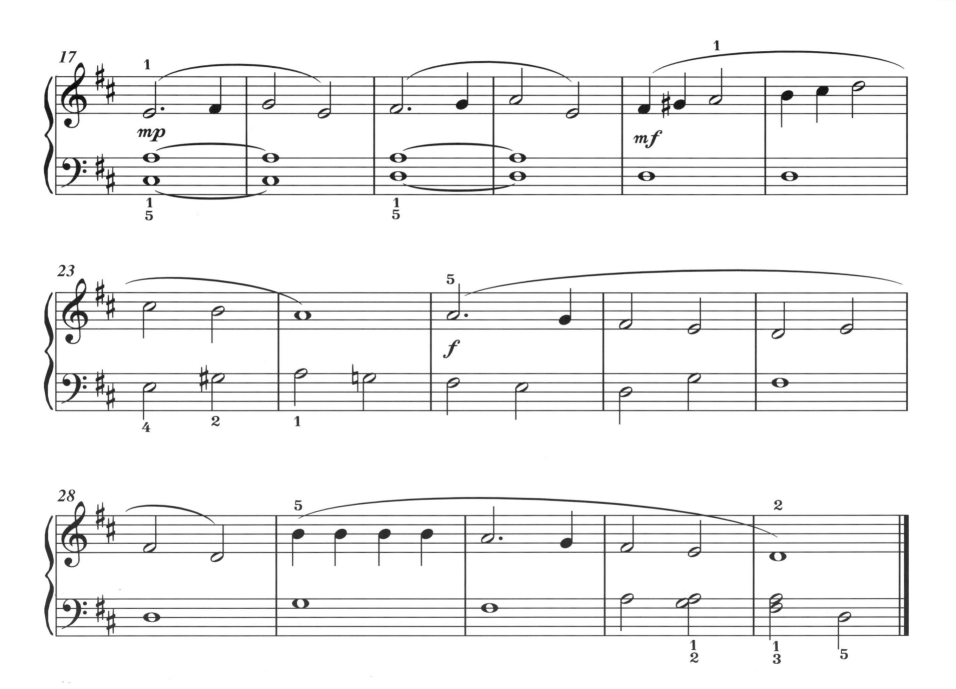

# Unto Us A Child Is Born

English traditional

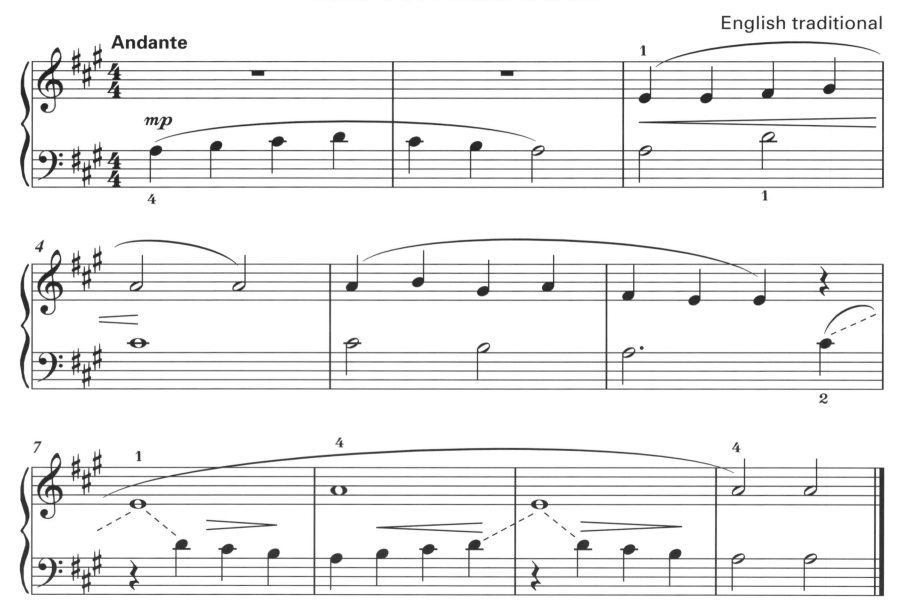

# Good Christian Men, Rejoice

Traditional German tune

# God Rest You Merry, Gentlemen

English traditional

# O Tannenbaum

German traditional

**Moderato**

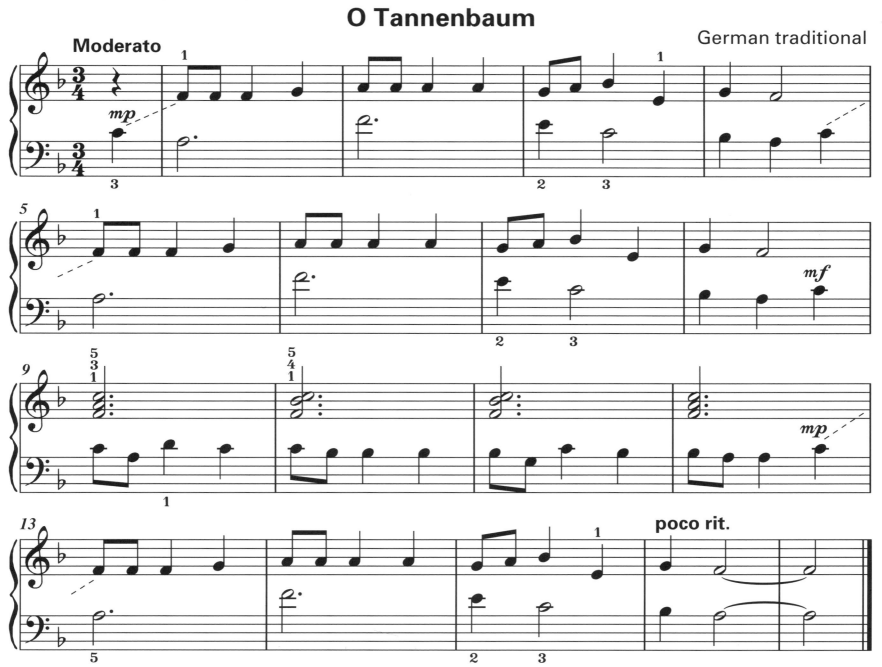

# Stille Nacht

Franz Grüber &
Joseph Mohr

# Ding Dong! Merrily On High

French traditional

# The Virgin Mary Had A Baby Boy

American spiritual

# The First Nowell

**Moderato**

English traditional